Nikolai
Rimsky-Korsakoff

Trombone Concerto

Tenor trombone
& piano

Reduction by Harold Perry

Boosey & Hawkes Music Publishers Ltd
www.boosey.com

This Concerto was originally written for Trombone and Military
Band. The Band parts are available on request.

★

Dieses Konzert ist für Posaune und Harmoniemusik geschrieben.
Die Harmoniestimmen sind über Verlangen erhältlich.

TROMBONE CONCERTO
for Tenor Trombone and Piano

N. RIMSKY-KORSAKOFF
Piano Reduction by
HAROLD PERRY

Sole Selling Agents: BOOSEY & HAWKES MUSIC PUBLISHERS Ltd.

A.S.M.P. 125

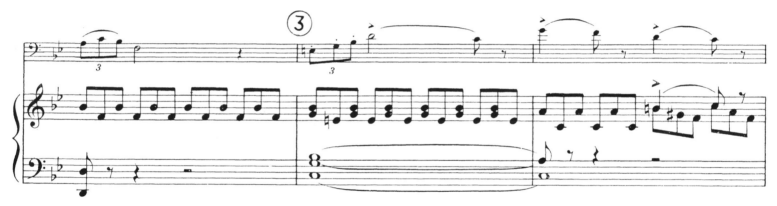

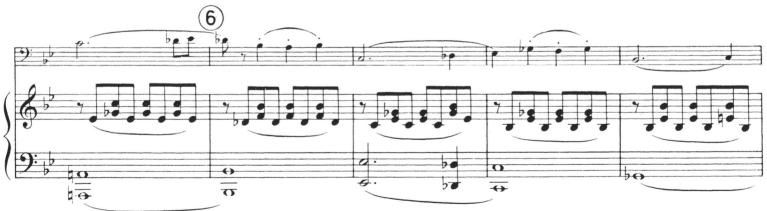

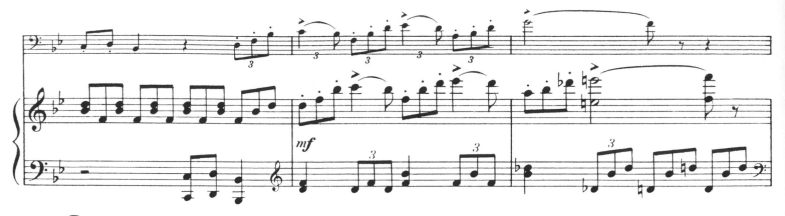

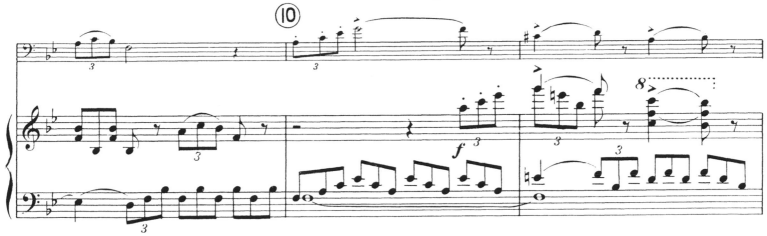

8

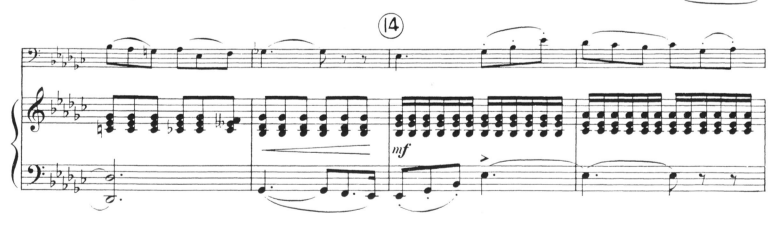

Tenor Trombone

Tenor Trombone

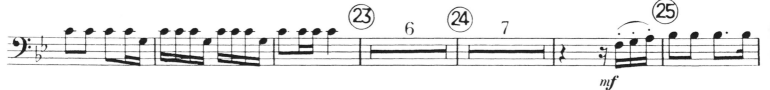

Tenor Trombone

TROMBONE CONCERTO
for Tenor Trombone and Piano

Tenor Trombone

N. RIMSKY-KORSAKOFF
Piano Reduction by
HAROLD PERRY

A.S.M.P. **125**

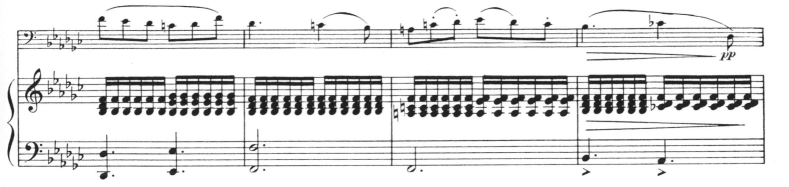

10

BOOSEY & HAWKES
MUSIC FOR BRASS ENSEMBLE

BERNSTEIN

Dance Suite
quintet with optional percussion

Presto Barbaro
(On the Waterfront)
brass, percussion and piano

Shivaree (A Fanfare)
double brass ensemble and percussion

BRITTEN

Fanfare for St. Edmundsbury
3 trumpets

CLACK, arr.

Carols for Brass
quartet/quintet

Folksongs
quartet/quintet

COLEBY

Rags
quintet

COPLAND

Ceremonial Fanfare
twelve part

Fanfare for the Common Man
twelve part

HARNIESS

Three Episodes
quintet

HERING, arr.

Early Classics
quartet

JACOB

Interlude
septet and percussion

MACDONALD

Sea Sketches
quintet

MAXWELL DAVIES

Strathclyde Concerto no. 3
trumpet, horn and piano reduction

NELSON

Fanfare for a Festival
septet and percussion

PROKOFIEFF

March from 'The Love of Three Oranges'
11 part and percussion

Two Pieces from 'Lieutenant Kijé'
14 part and percussion

ROSS

Trombone Quartet

SCHWERTSIK

Blechpartie
quintet

Horn Postille op. 46
4 horns

SHORT

Jazz Preludes
quartet

STONE

The Minstrels' Gallery
quartet

TELEMANN

Canons, Arias and Sonatas
2 trumpets

WASTALL, arr.

Session Time for Brass
for trumpet, trombone or French horn

BOOSEY & HAWKES

Boosey & Hawkes Music Publishers Limited